MIMOSA

MOVING INTO MATH

ACTIVITY BOOK

Contents

Name _____

For each picture, ask the child to:
- look at the animal
- draw a different animal in the empty box

Name_____

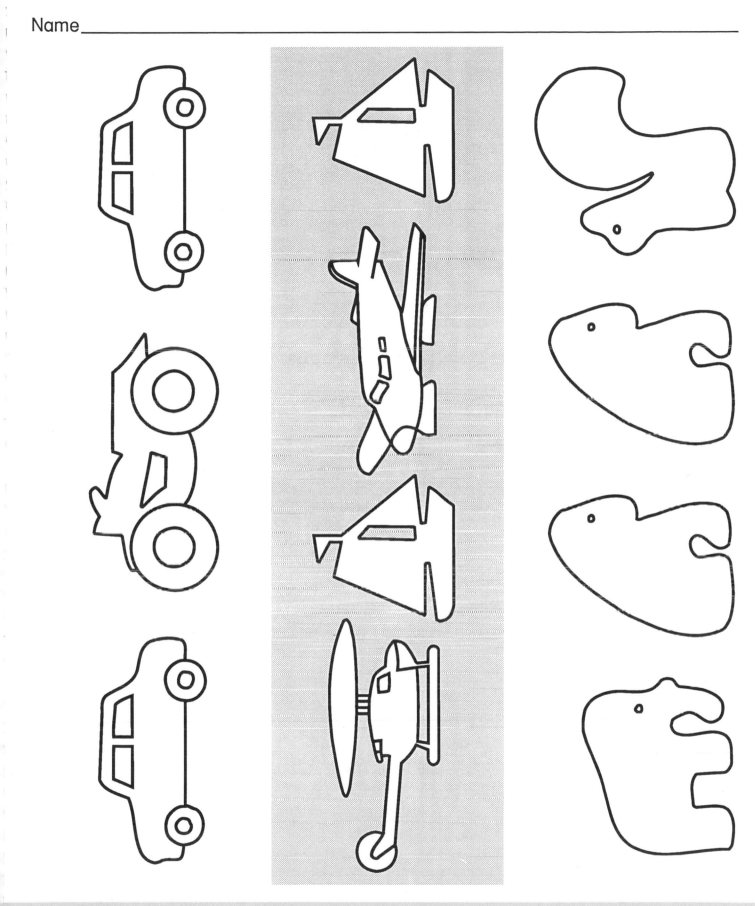

Ask the child to:
- turn the page sideways
- color the matching things in each row

Same attributes   *Use with Teachers' Resource Book page 53*   3

Name _____

For each row, ask the child to:
- put a ✓ on the pictures that are the same
- color the picture that is different

Same and different   *Use with Teachers' Resource Book page 55*

Name _____

Ask the child to:
- draw lines to match each picture with its outline
- color each outline and picture so that they look similar

Outline match   *Use with Teachers' Resource Book page 56*   5

Name _____

Ask the child to cut out the pictures from Cut-out page A. Then:
- paste the clown pictures near the clown that is already on this page
- sort the other pictures and choose another collection to paste on the page

Name _____

Ask the child to:
- look at the buttons at the top of the page
- find the buttons that belong to each shirt
- draw the buttons on the shirts

Sorting   *Use with Teachers' Resource Book page 62*

Name _____

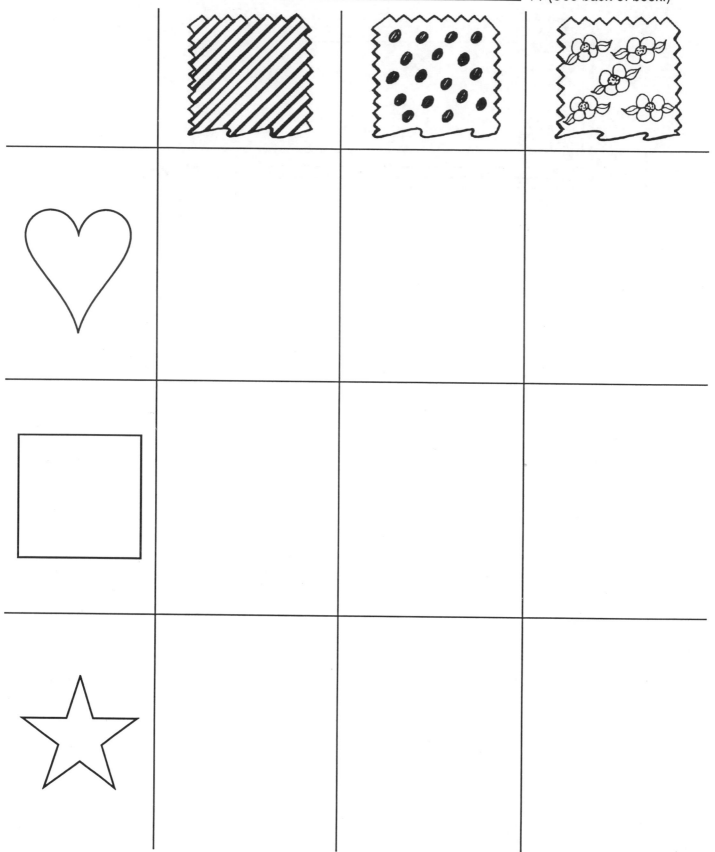

Ask the child to cut out the shapes from Cut-out page B. Then:
- look at each shape and decide where it should go on this chart
- paste each shape in the correct box

8   Two-attribute sorting   *Use with Teachers' Resource Book page 63*

Name_____

Ask the child to:
- draw two things that are the same in each shaded box
- draw two things that are different in each of the other boxes

Focusing on two   *Use with Teachers' Resource Book page 68*   9

Name

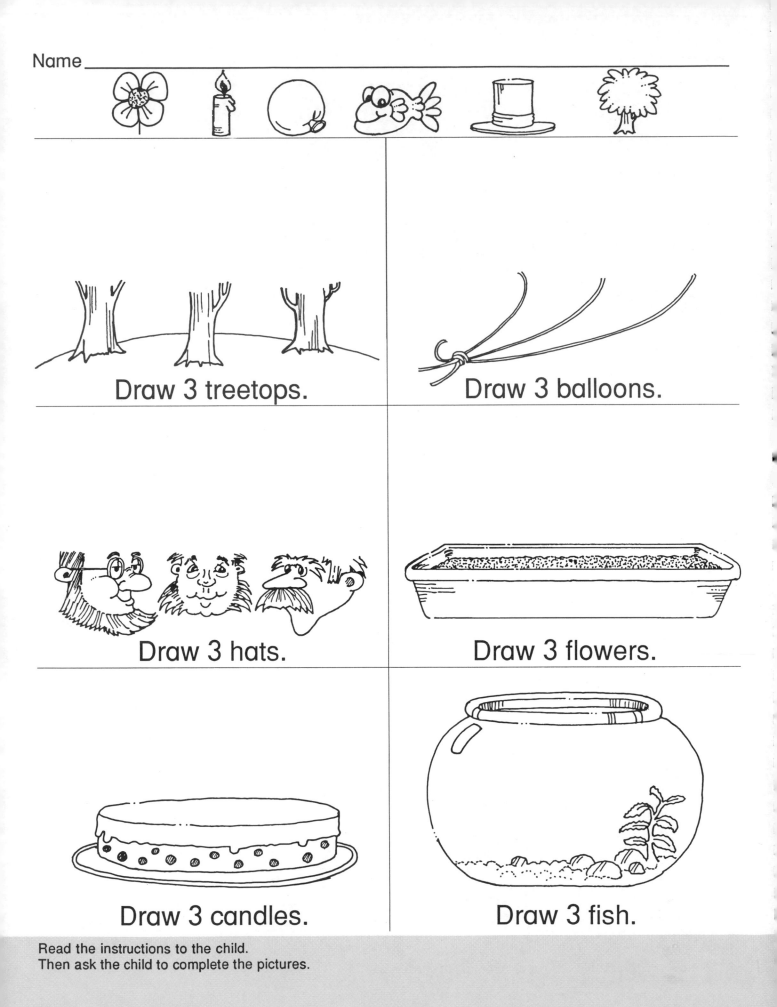

Draw 3 treetops.

Draw 3 balloons.

Draw 3 hats.

Draw 3 flowers.

Draw 3 candles.

Draw 3 fish.

Read the instructions to the child.
Then ask the child to complete the pictures.

Name_____

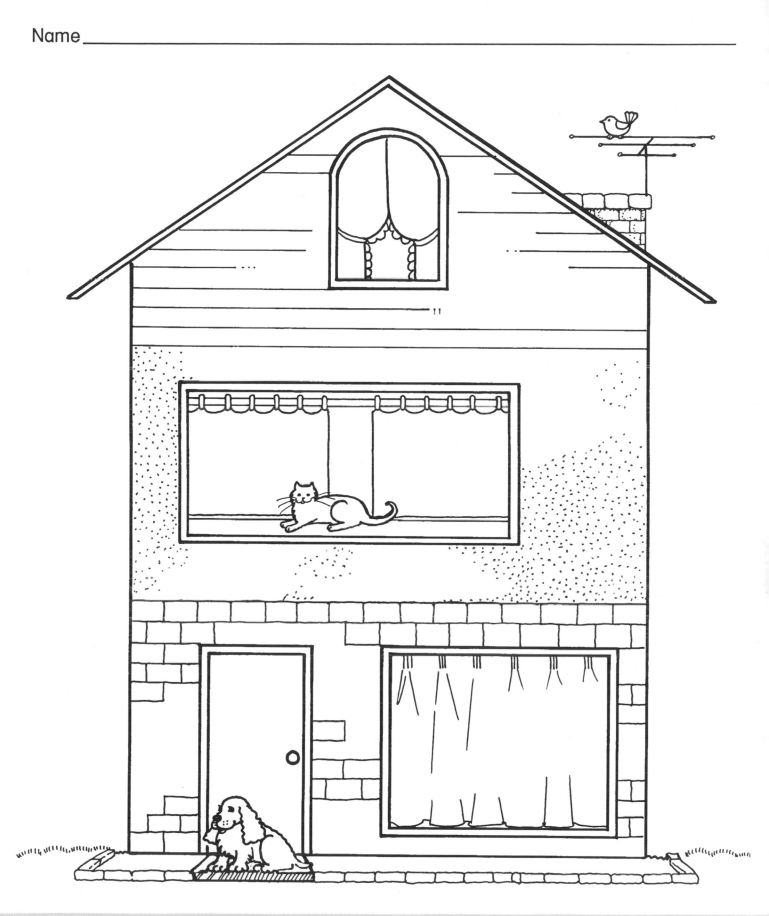

Ask the child to:
- color the curtain in the top window blue
- color the curtain in the bottom window yellow
- choose a different color for the curtains in the middle window
- talk about where the animals are

Positional language   *Use with Teachers' Resource Book page 81*

Name _____

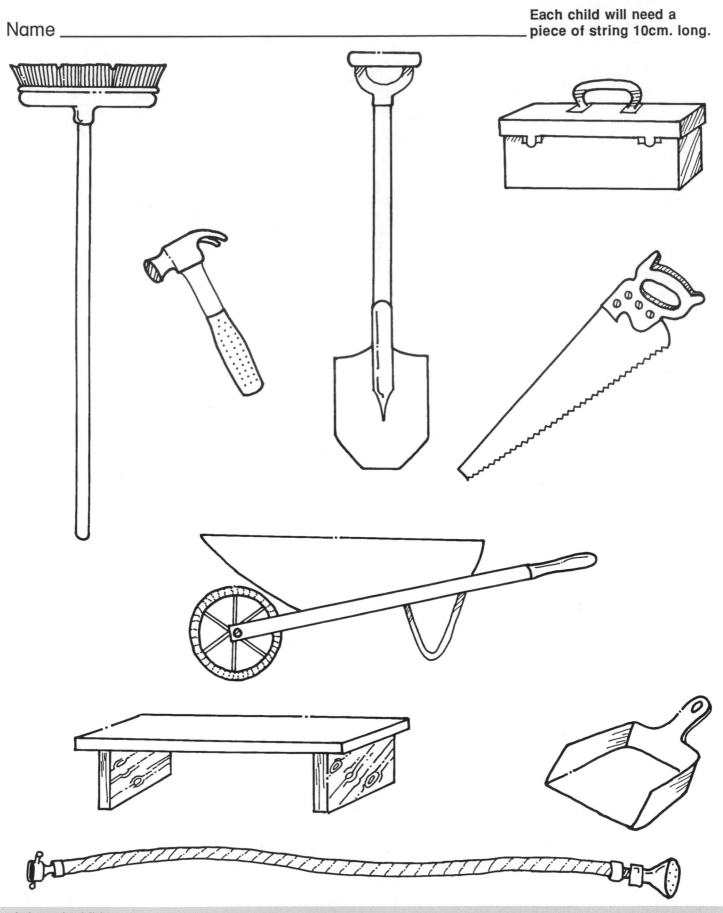

Ask each child to:
- compare each object with his or her length of string
- color the objects that are longer than the string
- ring the objects that are shorter than the string

Name _____

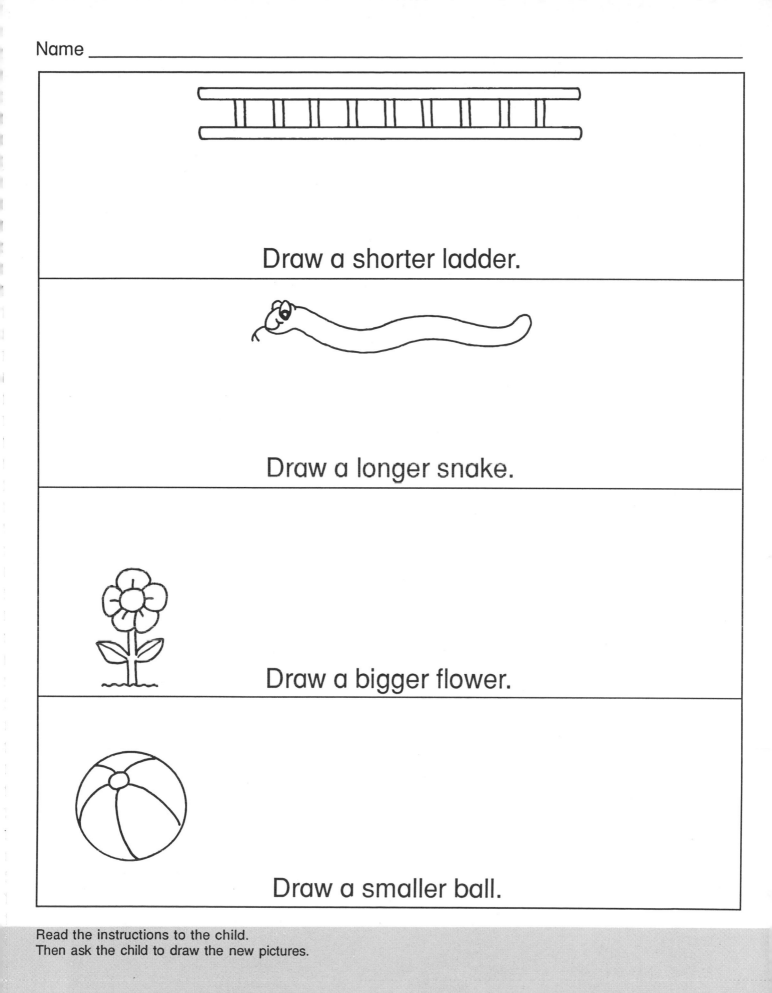

Draw a shorter ladder.

Draw a longer snake.

Draw a bigger flower.

Draw a smaller ball.

Read the instructions to the child.
Then ask the child to draw the new pictures.

Name _____

Ask the child to:
- count the animals in each group
- draw more animals to make each group have four

Name _____

Ask the child to:
- draw more pictures to make each row have five party things
- draw his or her own picture of five things at the bottom of the page

Focusing on five   *Use with Teachers' Resource Book page 156*   15

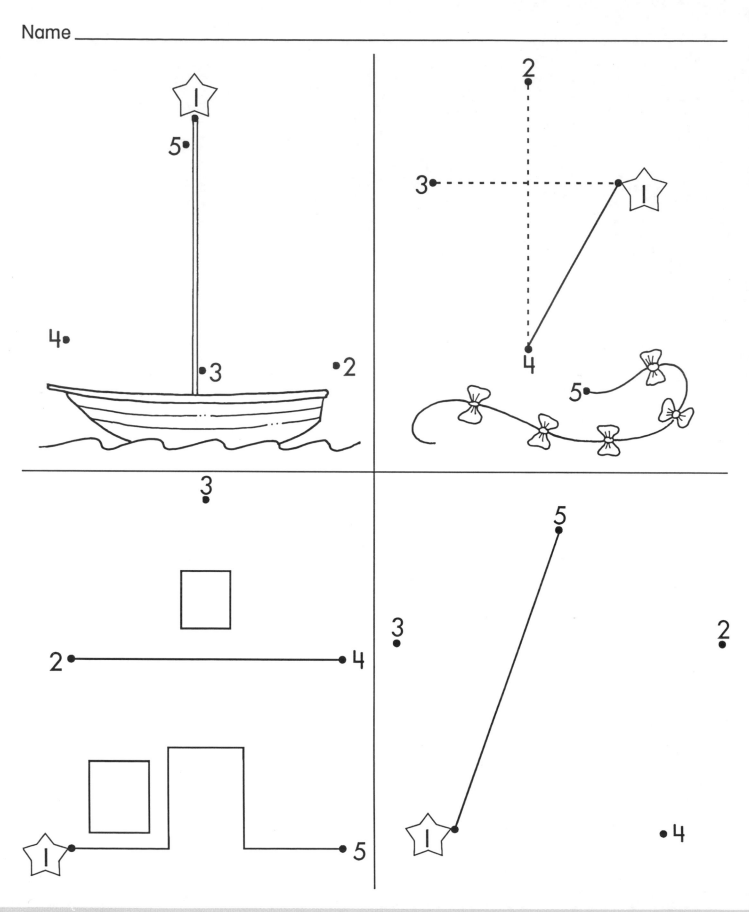

For each picture, ask the child to:
- find the number 1
- follow the numbers in order to complete the dot-to-dot picture

Name_____

Discuss the speech bubbles at the top of the page. Then ask the child to:
- look at the birthday cards in each column
- cross out the one that doesn't belong
- color the other cards

Number review   *Use with Teachers' Resource Book page 164*   17

Name_____

Ask the child to cut out the number words from the top of Cut-out page C. (Save the number symbols for page 19.)
Then ask the child to :
  • decide which number word belongs with each picture
  • paste each number word under the correct picture

Name _____

Ask the child to trace over the numbers on the bottom of Cut-out page C. Then:
  • cut out the numbers
  • decide which number belongs with each picture
  • paste each number in the correct box

Number symbols   *Use with Teachers' Resource Book page 166*

19

Name _____

Ask the child to:
 • find one shape with four sides and color it red
 • find one shape with three sides and color it blue
 • find one round shape and color it yellow
 • color the shapes that match in the same way

20   **Investigating shapes**   *Use with Teachers' Resource Book page 175*

Name_____

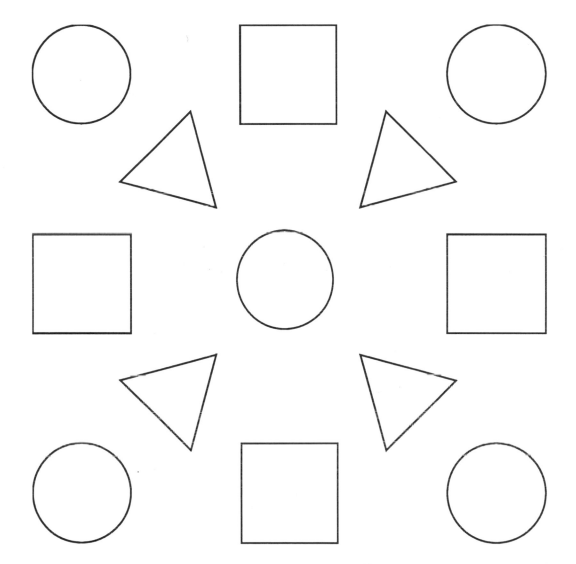

Ask the child to:
- trace over the outlines of the squares in red
- trace over the outlines of the triangles in green
- trace over the outlines of the circles in blue
- draw more squares, triangles, and circles in the pattern

Drawing shapes   *Use with Teachers' Resource Book page 177*   21

Draw more worms.

Draw fewer pumpkins.

Draw fewer strawberries.

Draw more birds.

Read the directions with the child, emphasizing *more* or *fewer*.
Then ask the child to draw the pictures.

Name _____

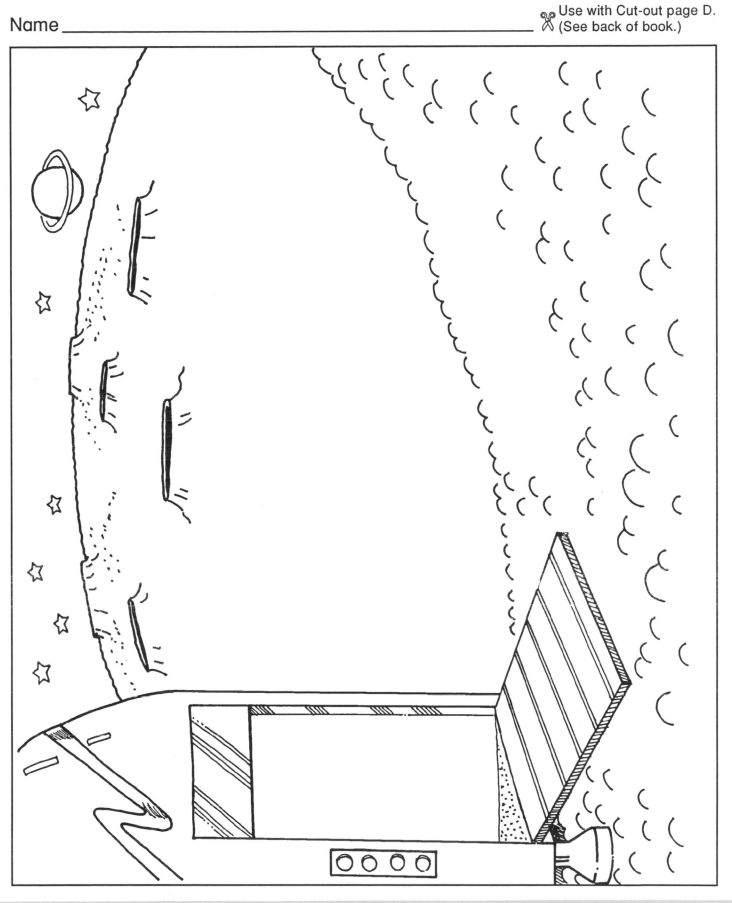

Ask the child to cut out the robots from Cut-out page D. (Save the ordinal words for page 24.) Then:
- read the signs on the robots
- paste the robots on the page so that they are walking into the spaceship in order

Ordinal position   *Use with Teachers' Resource Book page 189*   23

Name _____

✂ Use with Cut-out page D.
✂ (See back of book.)

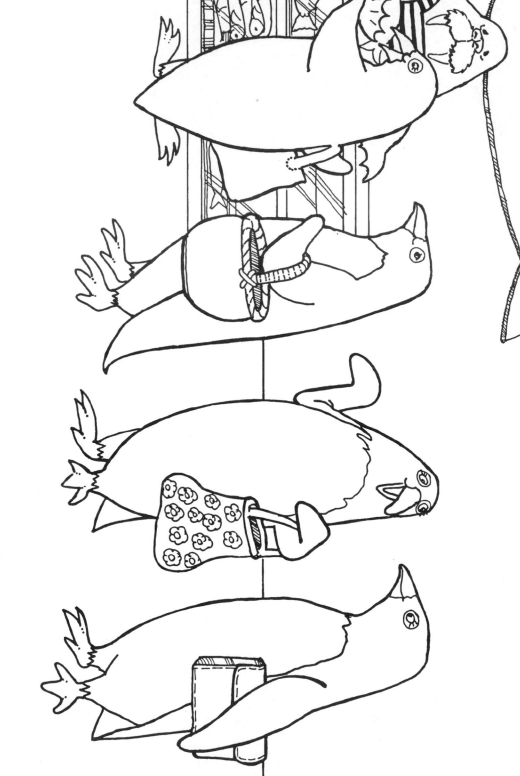

Ask the child to turn the page sideways. Then:
- put a ✓ on the penguin that is second in line; put a ✗ on the penguin that is first in line;
  ring the penguin that is last in line; color the penguin that is third in line.
- cut out the ordinal words from Cut-out page D and paste them in order under the penguins

Name _____

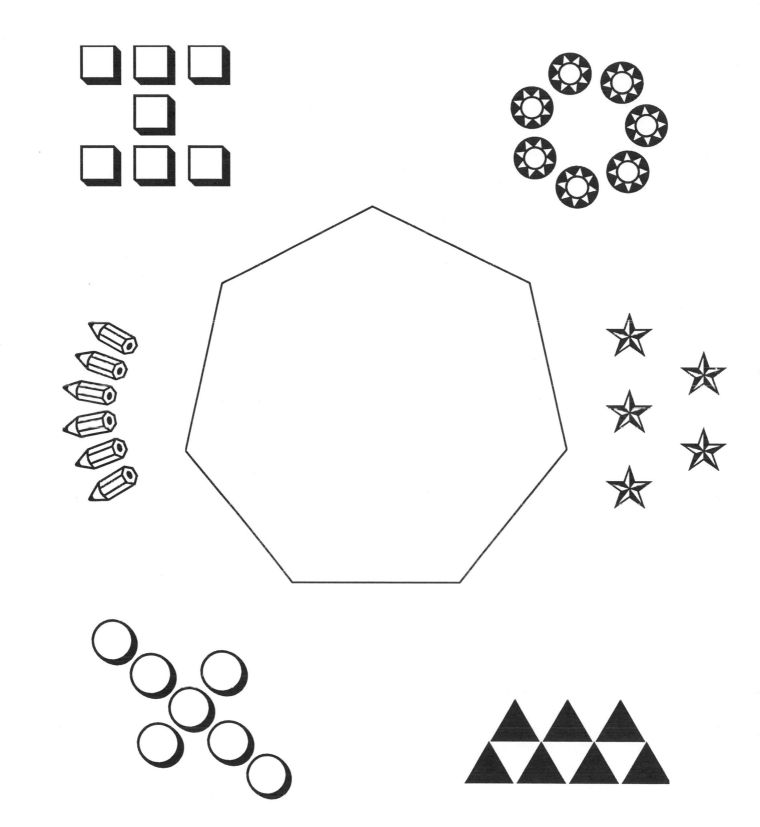

Ask the child to:
- draw a ring around each group of seven
- draw his or her own picture of seven things in the space in the center of the page

Focusing on seven   *Use with Teachers' Resource Book page 199*   25

Name_____

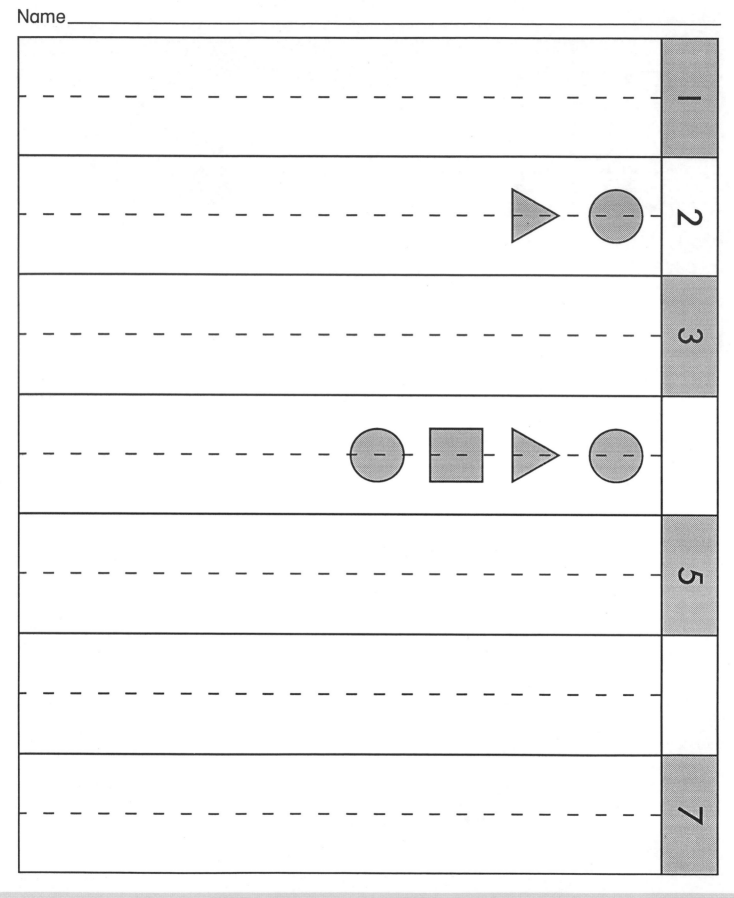

Ask the child to turn the page sideways. Then:
- draw hanging shapes for each number
- write the missing numbers

Name_____

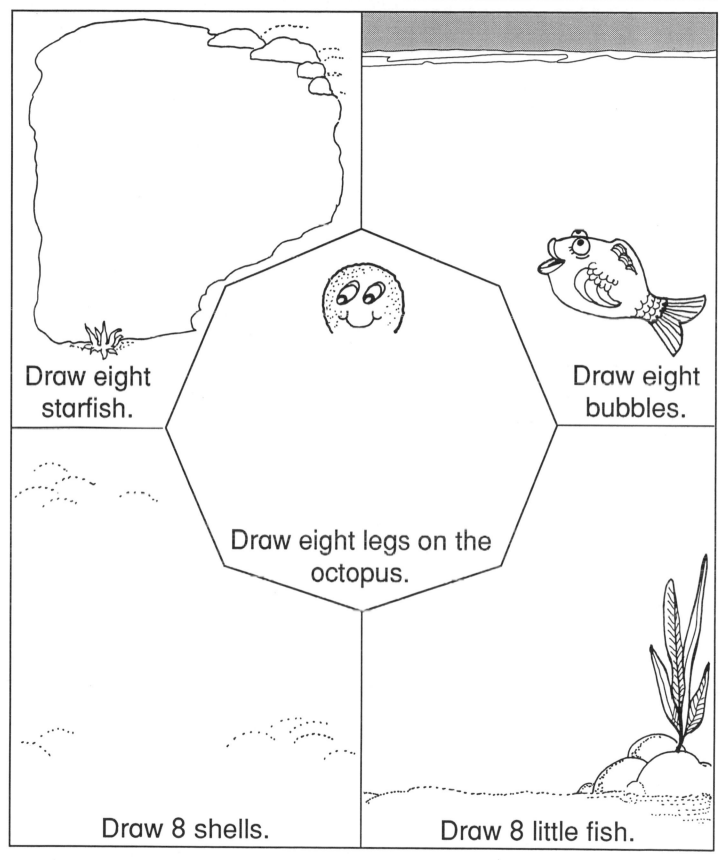

Draw eight
starfish.

Draw eight
bubbles.

Draw eight legs on the
octopus.

Draw 8 shells.

Draw 8 little fish.

Read the instructions with the child.
Then ask the child to complete the pictures.

Name _____

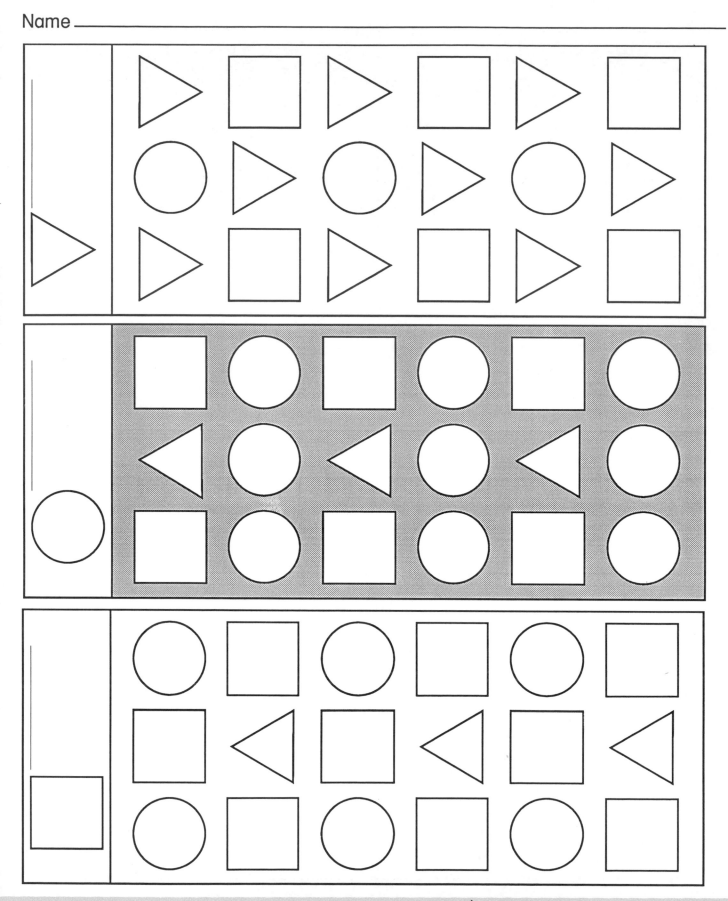

Ask the child to turn the page sideways. Point to the first section (with the △ at the bottom)
and ask the child to:
- color only those shapes in that section that match the shape at the bottom
- write how many shapes he or she colored

Repeat for the second section and the third section.

28   Focusing on nine   *Use with Teachers' Resource Book page 214*

Ask the child to:
- read the number words on the jars
- draw the correct number of peanuts in each jar

Name _____

Ask the child to:
- find the numbers that are hidden in the pictures
- trace over the numbers

30   **Reviewing number symbols**   *Use with Teachers' Resource Book page 220*

Name _____

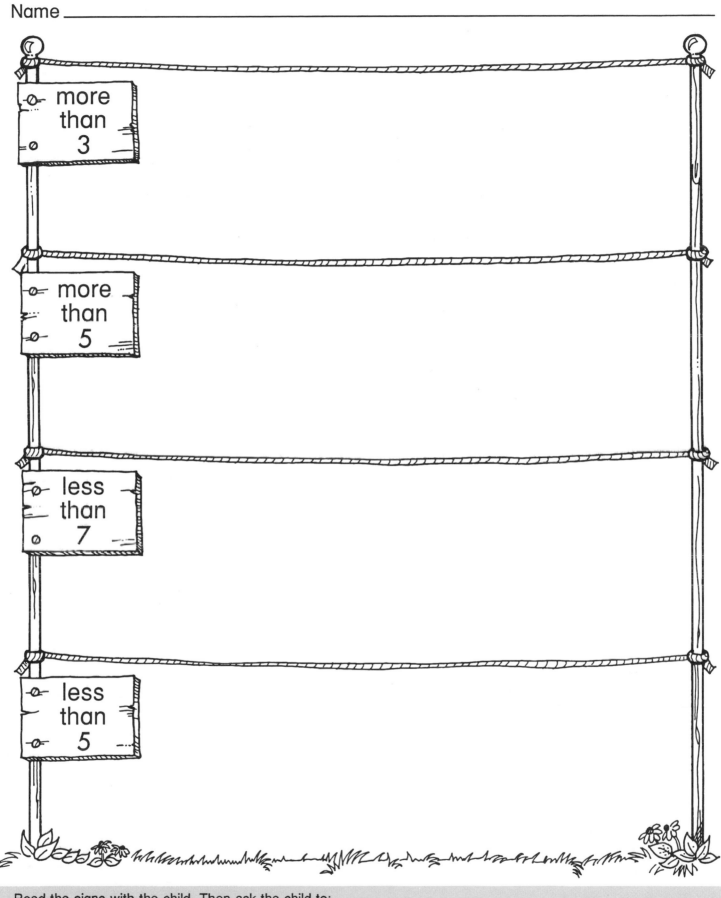

more
than
3

more
than
5

less
than
7

less
than
5

Read the signs with the child. Then ask the child to:
- draw things on each clothesline to match what the sign says
- tell how many things they drew on each clothesline

Comparing numbers   *Use with Teachers' Resource Book page 221*   31

Name _____

Put I more.

Put I more.

Put I more.

For each picture, ask the child to:
- place real links or counters on the page and tell how many
- put one more link or counter in the empty box
- count how many in all

Name _____

Telling addition stories   *Use with Teachers' Resource Book page 227*   33

Name _____

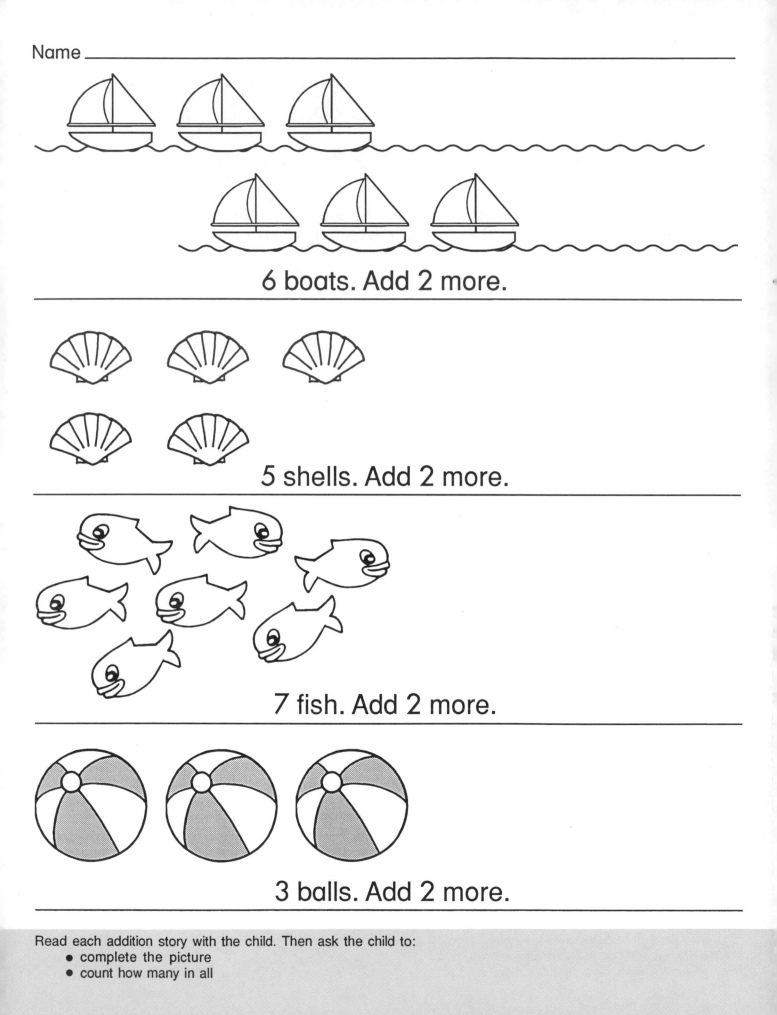

6 boats. Add 2 more.

5 shells. Add 2 more.

7 fish. Add 2 more.

3 balls. Add 2 more.

Read each addition story with the child. Then ask the child to:
- complete the picture
- count how many in all

Six rabbits. Two run away.

Seven muffins. One muffin is eaten.

Eight tickets. Two are sold.

Read each subtraction story to the child. Then ask the child to:
- place counters on each picture
- act out the story by taking away or covering up some of the counters

Exploring subtraction   *Use with Teachers' Resource Book page 233*

Name _____

Six sheep. Three run away.

Four kites. One blows away.

Seven balloons. Two pop.

Five. Take away two.

Name _____

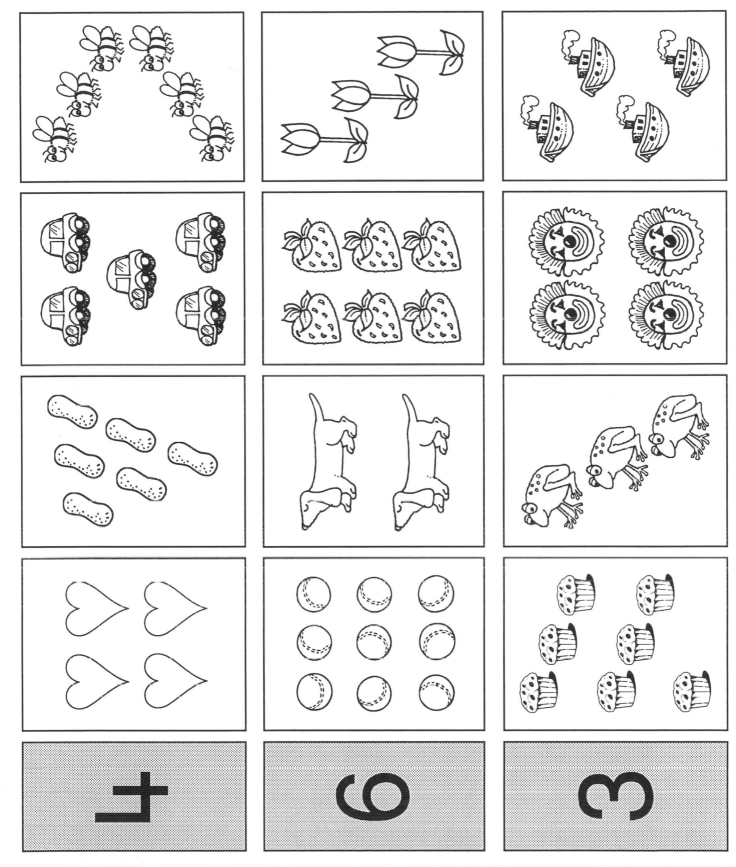

Ask the child to turn the page sideways. Then, for each row, ask the child to:
- read the number in the shaded box
- color the boxes that have **more** than that number

Comparing numbers   *Use with Teachers' Resource Book page 240*

5

9

Ask the child to cut out the kites from Cut-out page E. Then ask the child to turn this page sideways and:
- count the bows on the tails of the kites
- paste the kites in order on this page
- write the missing numbers

Name _____

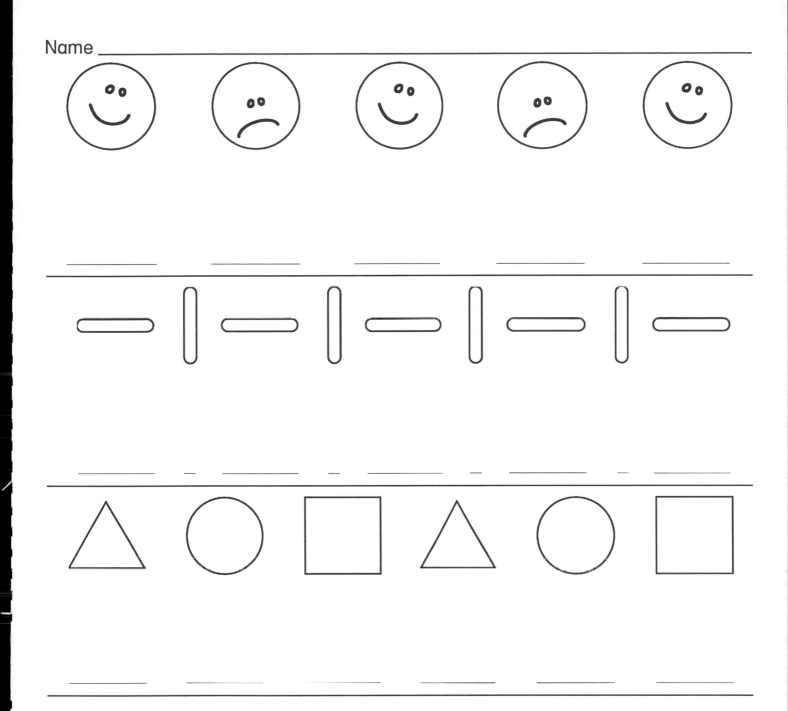

Draw your own pattern.

Ask the child to:
- copy each pattern
- draw his or her own pattern

Copying patterns   *Use with Teachers' Resource Book page 255*   39

Name _____

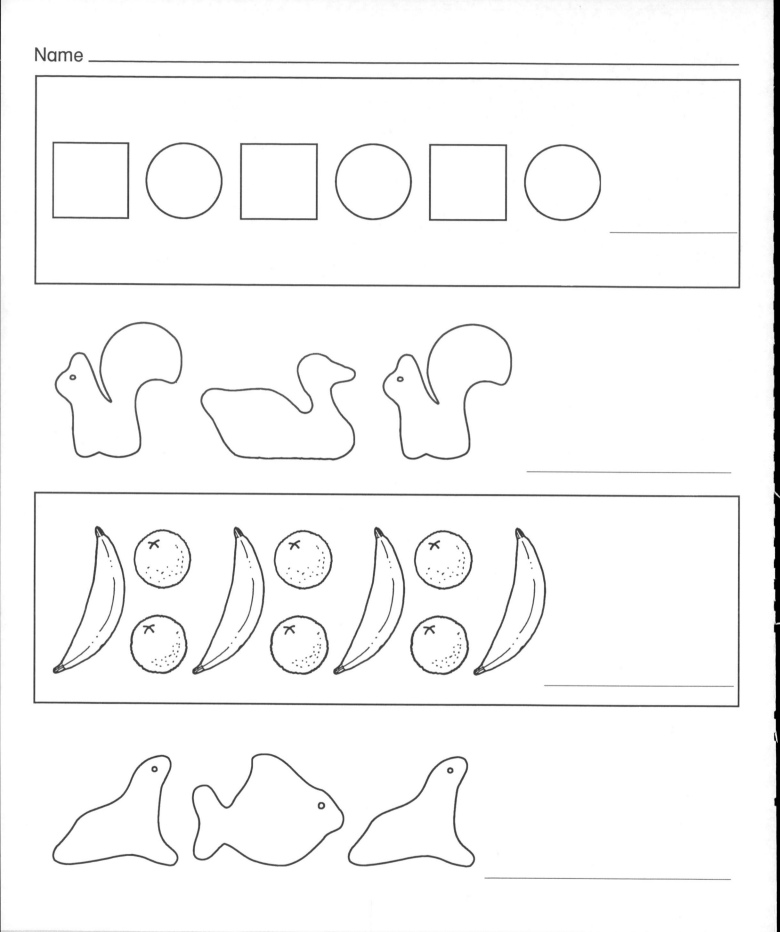

Ask the child to:
- look at each pattern and draw what comes next
- color each pattern

Name _____

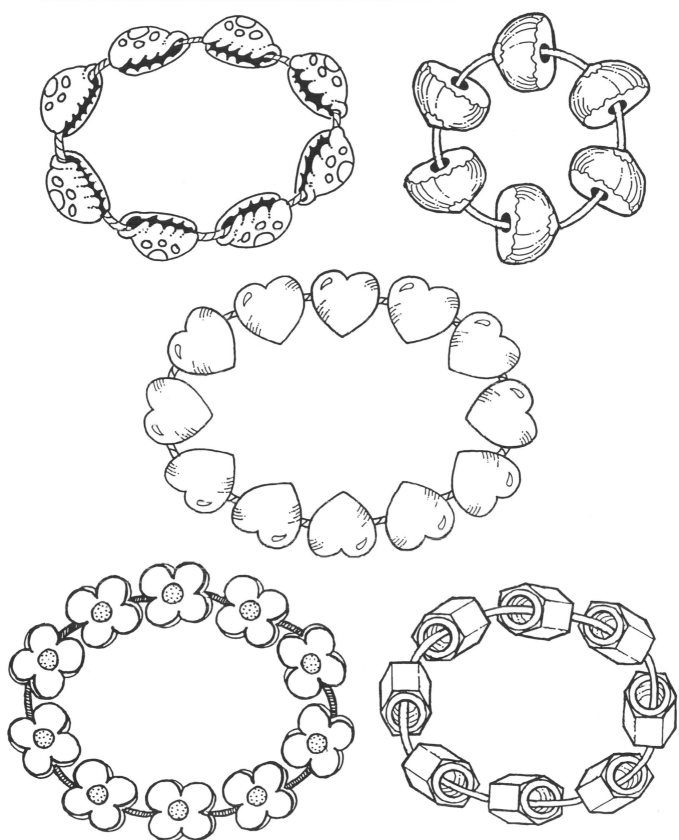

Ask the child to:
- color each group to make a pattern
- talk about the patterns with a friend

Creating patterns   *Use with Teachers' Resource Book page 259*   41

Name _____

2 bunches of five flowers.

2 baskets of seven eggs.

2 trays of eight cookies.

2 groups of four.

Read the number stories to the child.
Then ask the child to complete the pictures.

42   **Equal groups**   *Use with Teachers' Resource Book page 266*

Name _____

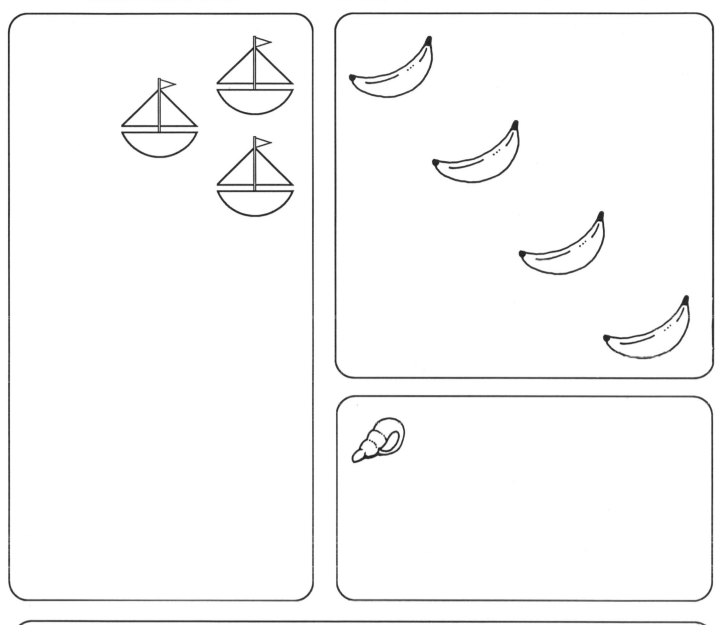

Ask the child to:
- count the pictures in each group
- draw more pictures to make each group have ten

Name _____

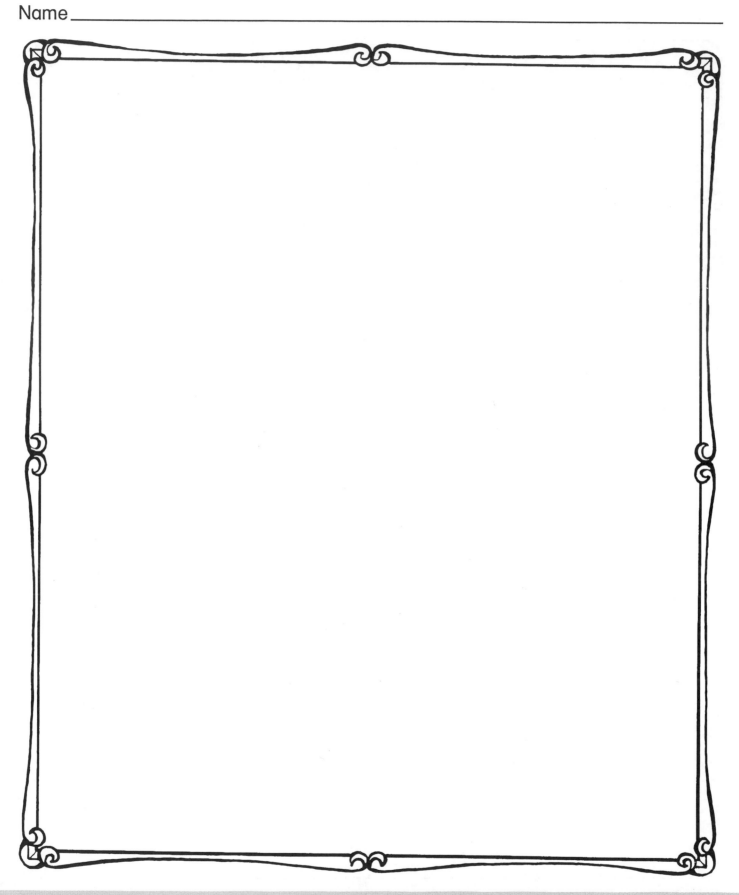

Ask the child to:
- use ten pattern blocks to make a design
- trace around the pattern blocks to draw the design

Name_____

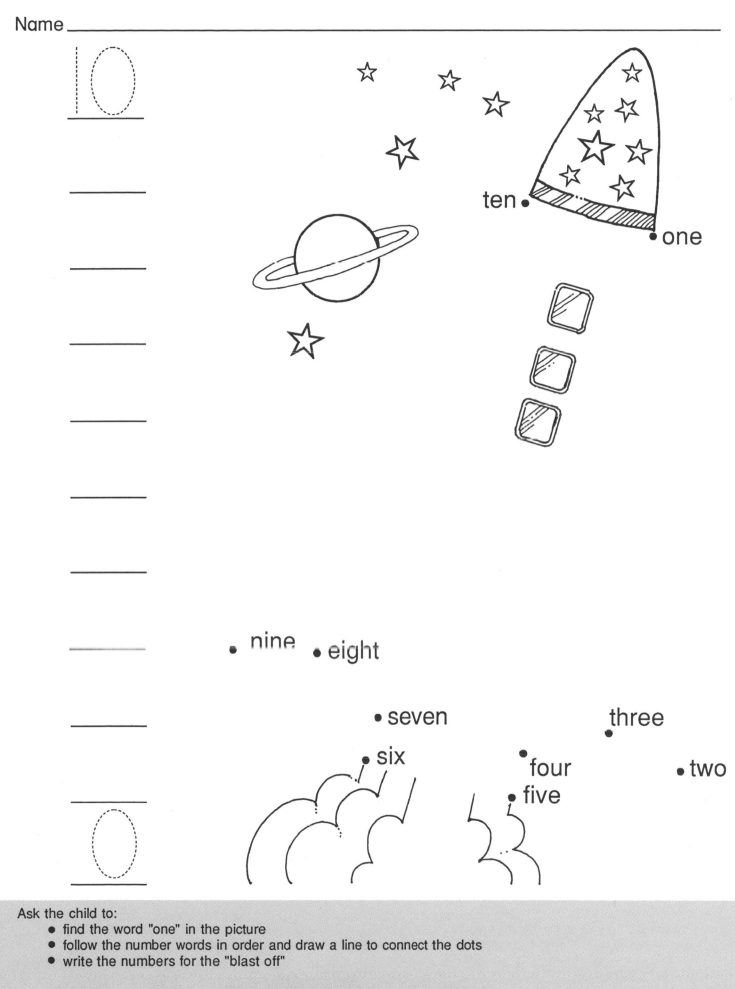

ten

one

nine · eight

seven

three

six

four

two

five

Numbers in order   *Use with Teachers' Resource Book page 280*   45

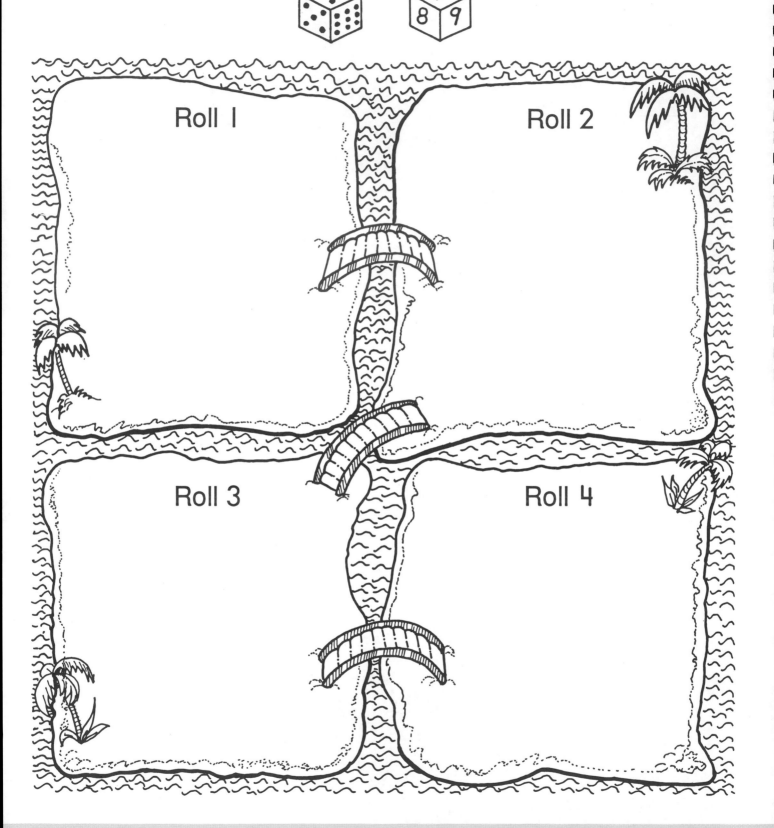

Roll 1

Roll 2

Roll 3

Roll 4

This game is played in pairs: **(1)** One child rolls the die; collects counters to match the number shown on the die; and places the counters in the "Roll 1" box on his or her page. **(2)** Now the other child rolls the die and collects counters for his or her "Roll 1" box. **(3)** The children take turns in this way until they have counters in all four boxes. **(4)** The children then compare their total counters to see who has more. **(5)** Discuss the various methods that the children used to figure out who "won" (e.g. sorting their counters into groups of ten and any "left-overs.")

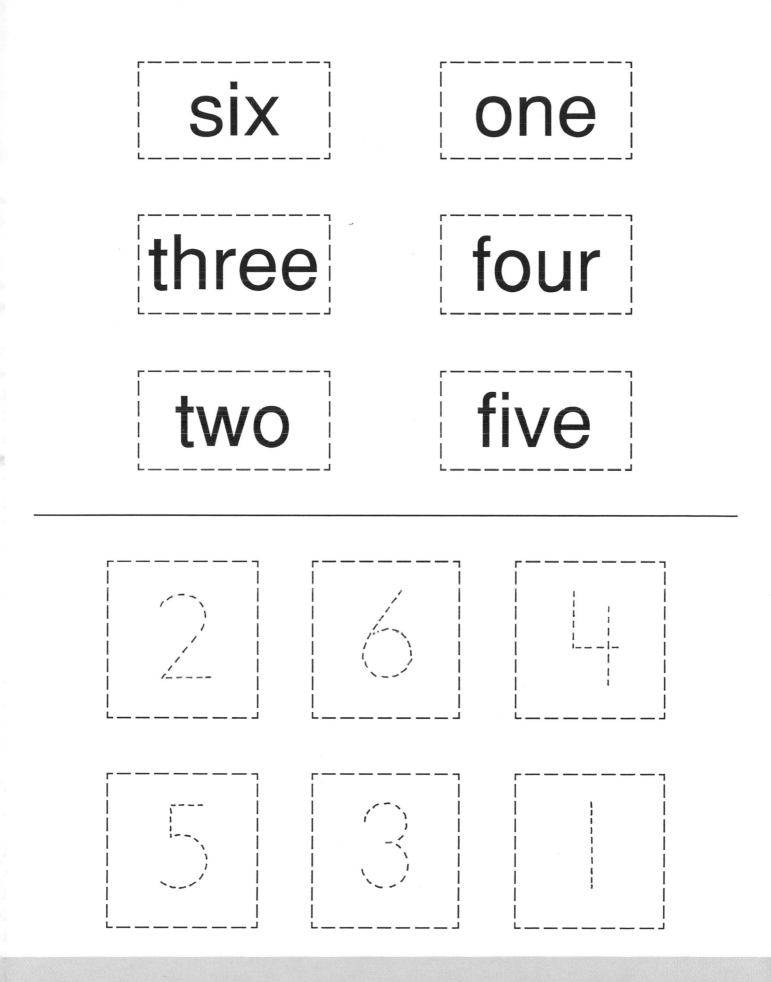

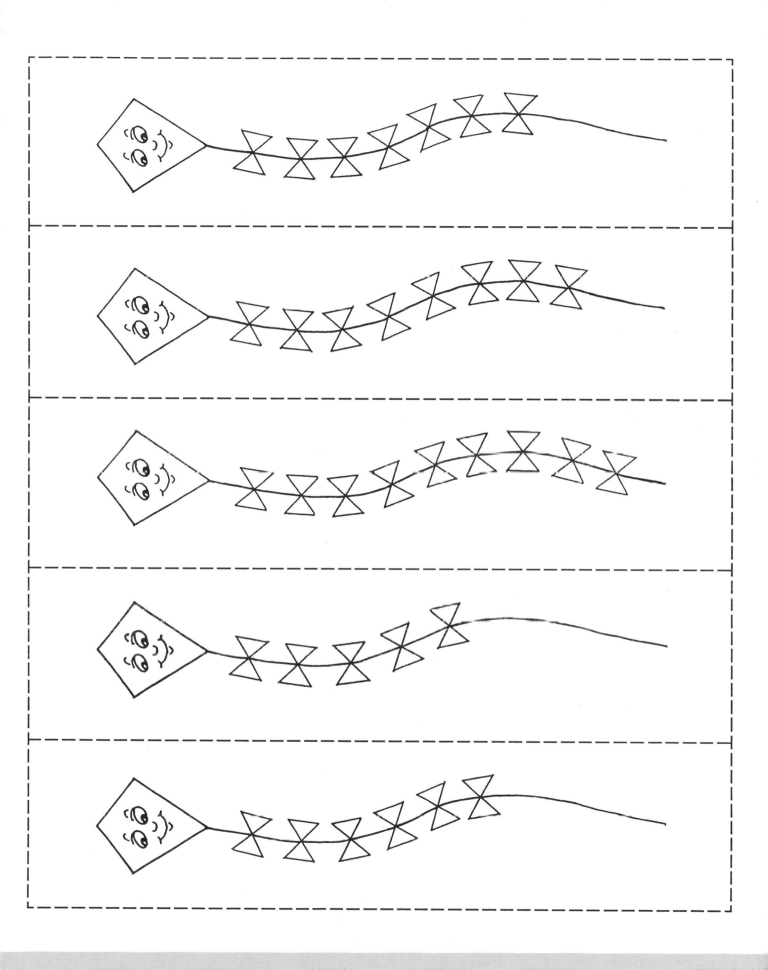